Carol J. Borsum

COMPUTERIZED ACCOUNTING

using **QUICKBOOKS PRO 2018**

FIFTH EDITION

Student Problems & Cases
Book 3 of 3

Images used on the front cover and throughout this book were obtained under license from Shutterstock.com.

© 2018
Copyright by Armond Dalton Publishers, Inc.
Okemos, Michigan

"QuickBooks Pro" is a registered trademark of Intuit Software in the United States and/or other countries and is used by Armond Dalton Publishers, Inc., under license from owner. *Computerized Accounting Using QuickBooks Pro 2018* is an independent publication not affiliated with Intuit Software.

ISBN 978-0-912503-71-4
Printed in the United States of America

TABLE OF CONTENTS

TABLE OF CONTENTS (continued)

Preparation for Question Pages

This book contains questions dealing with material in the Instructions book. Answer all questions in the answer spaces provided below each requirement or online at armonddaltonresources.com. *Consult your instructor about whether you are supposed to use this book's tear-out pages for your assigned homework or whether you should complete the homework online.*

Note that all pages in this book are on perforated pages to enable you to tear out the question/problem pages and hand them in to your instructor if you are not using the online grading portion of armonddaltonresources.com. It will be more convenient if you tear out all question/problem pages for each chapter as you go. Be sure to write your name in the space provided at the top of each question/problem page before handing it in.

Some of the chapters in this project include problems and print requirements, as well as questions. While questions usually require only a written answer in the spaces provided, problems often include printouts of solution material from the software. Be sure to include your name and the problem number on all question/problem pages and printouts that you hand in to the instructor if you are completing your assignments using the tear-out pages.

Because of practice exercises and chapter problems as you work with the Instructions book, each of you may have different transactions and balances in the company data sets used in those exercises. It is important that you start the problem material for each chapter with clean versions of the sample companies. In order to ensure this, before you start the problem material for each chapter, you will need to restore both Rock Castle Construction and Larry's Landscaping & Garden Supply data sets from the initial backups that you downloaded from the Armond Dalton Resources website. Refer to the "Restore Company Backup Files" section of the E-materials located at www.armonddaltonresources.com. After restoring both companies, you can then proceed to the question and problem material for each chapter.

Name:

2 Chapter Familiarization

As described on page v of this book, you should restore both Rock Castle Construction and Larry's Landscaping & Garden Supply using the initial backups that you downloaded from the Armond Dalton Resources website. Restore both companies before working on this chapter's questions and problem material. If you cannot recall how to restore a backup, refer to the section "Restore Company Backup Files" in the E-materials located at www.armonddaltonresources.com.

PART I – QUESTIONS

Q-2-1. Transaction cycles

Required

Which of the following is **not** a transaction cycle that you will use in these materials?

1. Sales and cash receipts (Customers in *QuickBooks*)
2. Purchases and cash disbursements (Vendors in *QuickBooks*)
3. Human Resources (HR Essentials in *QuickBooks*)
4. Payroll (Employees in *QuickBooks*)
5. Inventory

Q-2-2. Menu bar and Icon bar

Required

a. Which of the following is a true statement about the differences between the Menu bar and the Icon bar?

1. The Icon bar is located at the top of the main *QuickBooks* window.

2. There are more options available through the Menu bar than through the Icon bar.

3. The Home Page can only be accessed through the Icon bar.

4. The Menu bar is located on the left side of the main *QuickBooks* window.

5. None of the above statements are true.

b. Which Menu bar item is used most extensively in these materials?

_____

Q-2-3.　Icon bar activities

Required

Which Icon bar icon is used most extensively in these materials?

_____

Q-2-4.　Vendor Center

Required

a. Which of the following is *not* a way to open the Vendor Center?
   1. Click Vendors on the Menu bar, then click Vendor Center from the list of menu items.
   2. Click the Vendors button in the middle of the Home Page.
   3. Click the Reports menu and then click Vendors & Payables.
   4. Click the Vendors icon on the Icon bar.
   5. All of the above are ways to open the Vendor Center.

b. Which tab in the Vendor Center would you use to change the payment terms for a vendor?

_____

Q-2-5.　Home Page icons

Required

a. Which Home Page icon is used to record a cash sale to a customer?

_____

b. Which Home Page icon is used to record the receipt of inventory with a bill from the vendor?

_____

   c. Which Home Page icon is used to pay employees by check?

_____

   d. Which Home Page icon is used to issue a credit memo to a customer for returned goods?

_____

   e. Which Home Page icon is used to record a cash receipt from a customer for an outstanding sales invoice?

_____

   f. Which Home Page icon is used to write a check to a vendor for an expense that has not previously been recorded as an account payable?

_____

Q-2-6. Finding information in *QuickBooks*

An important feature of any software package is the degree of "user friendliness" that the software has built in to help new users understand the software more easily. *QuickBooks* has a substantial amount of such "user friendliness." These questions exercise your ability to find relevant information that may or may not have been discussed thoroughly in the chapter.

Required

   a. What is the amount of the last sales invoice for Kristy Abercrombie, a customer of Rock Castle Construction?

_____

   b. Which Rock Castle Construction customer owes the company the highest amount of money as of 12/15/2022?

_____

c. Dan T. Miller works for Rock Castle Construction. What is his address?

_____

d. What is Rock Castle Construction's net income this fiscal quarter to date (10/01/2022 to 12/15/2022)?

_____

e. As of 12/15/2022 how many total cabinet pulls did Rock Castle Construction have on hand?

_____

Q-2-7. Names of *QuickBooks* buttons and icons
Required

Provide the name of each of the following *QuickBooks* buttons and icons.

Button/Icon	Name
☑	
◉	
▼	
📅	
▭	
Export...	
🖨	

Name:

PART II: PROBLEMS AND REPORTS/PRINTOUTS

P-2-1.   Changing companies

▶ *Open QuickBooks and Larry's Landscaping & Garden Supply. Then, switch from Larry's Landscaping & Garden Supply to Rock Castle Construction.*

Required

List the steps you followed to change companies from Larry's Landscaping & Garden Supply to Rock Castle Construction.

_____

_____

_____

_____

_____

P-2-2.   Customer Center activities

Required

For each of the following activities in the Customer Center, state the tab, item on a list, and/or icon you will use to perform the activity. In some cases, you will need more than one of these.

a. State the tab, item on a list, and/or icon you will use to perform maintenance for a new customer.

_____

b. State the tab, item on a list, and/or icon you will use to prepare a list of all sales invoices for a period of time without printing the list.

_____

_____

_____

_____

c. State the tab, item on a list, and/or icon you will use to print a list of all active customers, including the account balance receivable from each customer.

_____

_____

_____

_____

d. State the tab, item on a list, and/or icon you will use to export a list of all sales invoices for a period of time to Excel.

_____

_____

_____

_____

_____

_____

Name:

P-2-3. Print or not print a document

▶ *Click the Create Invoices icon on the Home Page and examine the window that is opened to determine if there is a print icon. Is there a print icon?*

▶ *Click the Pay Bills icon on the Home Page and examine the window that is opened to determine if there is a print icon. Is there a print icon?*

Required

Explain why there is a print icon on one of the windows and not the other.

_____

_____

_____

_____

P-2-4. Differences in *QuickBooks* terms

Required

Explain the difference between the following:

a. Home icon and Home Page

_____

_____

b. Maintenance and processing information

_____

_____

_____

Name:

c. Menu bar and Icon bar

_____

_____

_____

_____

_____

_____

d. Vendor Center and Employee Center

_____

_____

_____

_____

_____

_____

_____

Name:

P-2-5. Default information

Required

a. Briefly explain what is meant by default information.

_____

_____

_____

_____

b. What is the purpose of having default information in *QuickBooks*?

_____

_____

_____

_____

Name:

P-2-6.   Purposes of *QuickBooks* buttons and icons

Required

State the purpose of each of the following buttons or icons:

Button/Icon	Name	Purpose
✔	Check box	
◉	Radio button	
▼	Drop-down list arrow	
📅	Date button	
☐	Text box	
Export...	Export button	
🖶	Print icon	

Name:

3 Chapter — Maintenance, Processing Information, and Internal Controls

As described on page v of this book, you should restore both Rock Castle Construction and Larry's Landscaping & Garden Supply using the initial backups that you downloaded from the Armond Dalton Resources website. Restore both companies before working on this chapter's problem material. If you cannot recall how to restore a backup, refer to the section "Restore Company Backup Files" in the E-materials located at www.armonddaltonresources.com.

PART I – QUESTIONS

Maintenance

Q-3-1.   Waren Sports Supply

Required

a. What is the credit limit for the customer University of Southern Iowa?

_____

b. Which tab of the Edit Customer window would you use to change the payment terms for a customer?

_____

c. What is the street address for the employee Nancy Ford?

_____

d. What is the cost for the inventory item FB-027, shoulder pad set?

_____

Name:

Q-3-2. Rock Castle Construction

Required

a. What are the Terms (payment terms) for a credit to sales for a sale to the customer Sonya Bristol?

_____

b. How many general ledger subaccounts for the Repairs expense account (account #64200) does Rock Castle Construction have?

_____

c. What is the current Salary amount for Dan T. Miller? (*Hint*: After you open the Edit Employee window for Miller, select Payroll Info.)

_____

d. Change the Salary amount for Dan T. Miller to $42,500.00 and click OK to save the changes. After the change, reopen his employee record and view the Salary amount. Is it the same as the one you entered when you changed it?

_____

Name:

Transaction Processing

Q-3-3.   Overview of processing information

Required

a. Which of the two tasks is done first – maintenance or processing transactions?

_____

_____

_____

_____

_____

b. Which of the following activities involves transaction processing in the sales and collection cycle?

      I.   Receiving a customer payment
     II.   Adding a new customer
   III.   Purchasing inventory
   IV.   Billing customers
    V.   Preparing a payroll check
   VI.   Entering the date of a cash sale
  VII.   Preparing a credit memo for goods returned

1. I, IV, V, and VI

2. I, II, V, and VII

3. I, IV, VI and VII

4. All of the above

5. None of the above

c. Assume you have just opened a company and want to begin processing transactions. In the table below, identify which icon on the Home Page you will select to process each of the transaction types. The first row is provided as an example.

Transaction Type	Home Page Icon Button
Prepare a sales invoice	*Create Invoices*
Deposit today's receipts	
Receive inventory	
Record employee's time worked	
Order new inventory	
Issue credit for returned goods on a sale	

Q-3-4.   Examining sales invoices for Rock Castle Construction

Required

a. What is the total amount of Invoice No. 1023 for Linda Rice?

_____

b. How much was billed for removing a fallen tree on Invoice No. 1023 for Linda Rice?

_____

c. Was there sales tax included on Invoice No. 1023 for Linda Rice?

_____

d. What amount will be credited to sales for Invoice No. 1023 for Linda Rice?

_____

Q-3-5. Processing sales invoices for Rock Castle Construction

Required

a. Assuming Rock Castle Construction wants to issue sales invoice numbers sequentially, what should the next invoice number be?

_____

b. What is the source of information *QuickBooks* uses for the selling price for inventory items sold to customers?

1. Chart of accounts
2. Previous maintenance performed in the Edit Items window
3. Reports
4. All of the above
5. None of the above

c. Which document is the person processing sales invoice transactions likely to use to obtain the customer name and type of services desired by the customer?

1. Sales invoice
2. Shipping document
3. Customer purchase order
4. Remittance advice
5. None of the above

Name:

Internal Controls

Q-3-6.   Internal controls

Required

a. Which of the following is the best description of automatic entry controls?

1. Automatic entry controls automatically calculate and post information after the person entering the data has entered other information or clicked certain buttons.

2. Automatic entry controls automatically enter information after receiving a cue from the person entering the data.

3. Automatic entry controls inform the person entering data that information needed to process the transaction has been omitted.

4. Automatic entry controls provide error messages when invalid data is entered.

5. None of the above

b. What is the main purpose of automatic calculation and posting controls?

1. Automatic calculation and posting controls increase the amount of documentation in the system.

2. Automatic calculation and posting controls decrease the amount of documentation in the system.

3. Automatic calculation and posting controls enhance the segregation of duties in the system.

4. Automatic calculation and posting controls reduce the likelihood of errors in the system.

5. None of the above

Q-3-7. Automatic entry controls – Rock Castle Construction

Required

▶ *Click the Enter Bills icon on the Home Page to open the Enter Bills window. Before selecting a vendor, look carefully at the window. Now select C.U. Electric in the Vendor box.*

Which of the following lists include the boxes in the Enter Bills window that changed after you selected C.U. Electric in the Vendor box? Include boxes with contents that have changed, as well as boxes that were previously blank that now have information in them (automatic entry control entries).

1. Address, Terms, Memo, and Bill Due boxes
2. Address, Terms, Ref. No., and Bill Due boxes
3. Address, Terms, and Bill Due boxes
4. Address, Terms, Bill Due, and Account (Expense tab)
5. None of the above

Q-3-8. Automatic calculation and posting controls – Rock Castle Construction

Required

▶ *Open the Enter Bills window and select the Items tab. Enter the following for the vendor Patton Hardware Supplies, but do not save the transaction:*

- Light Pine Cabinets for Item and 2 for Qty.
- Doorknobs Std for Item and 5 for Qty.

Name:

a. Which of the following is a true statement related to the automatic calculation and posting controls resulting from the entries you made for the items to be purchased from Patton Hardward Supplies?

1. The Amount box contents are the result of an automatic entry control.

2. The Amount Due box contents are the result of an automatic calculation control.

3. The Amount box contents are the result of an automatic calculation control.

4. Both 2 and 3 are correct.

5. None of the above are correct.

b. Which of the following is the correct accounting entry that would be made if you had saved the transaction you started entering for Patton Hardware Supplies?

1. DR. Inventory Asset $3,075.00
       CR. Cost of Goods Sold $3,075.00

2. DR. Cost of Goods Sold $3,075.00
       CR. Inventory Asset $3,075.00

3. DR. Inventory Asset $3,075.00
       CR. Accounts Payable $3,075.00

4. DR. Inventory Asset $3,075.00
       CR. Job Expenses $3,075.00

5. None of the above are correct.

Name:

PART II – PROBLEMS AND REPORTS/PRINTOUTS

Maintenance

P-3-1.   **Maintenance information for Larry's Landscaping & Garden Supply**

Required

a. Attempt to delete the Customer: Job Ecker Design. What is the message when you attempt to delete it?

_____

_____

b. Why do you believe there is a control preventing you from deleting Customer: Job, such as Ecker Design?

_____

_____

_____

_____

_____

_____

c. Add the following general ledger account. (*Hint:* Type the information and press [Enter] or use the drop-down lists when available to select the correct information.)

- **Account Type:** Accounts Receivable
- **Account Name and Description:** Receivables from Employees

How many entries did you type and how many did you select using the drop-down list?

Transaction Processing

P-3-2. Processing sales invoices for Larry's Landscaping & Garden Supply

Required

▶ *Process Sales Invoice No. 142 on Purchase Order 2559 for the sale of the following items on 12/19/2022 to Jennifer Hermann - Residential Maintenance Customer: Job. If you receive a message about the customer exceeding its credit limit, click Yes to continue.*

- 3 Pumps (Fountain pumps)
- 25 Sprkl pipes (Plastic sprinkler piping)

Print the sales invoice.

P-3-3. Additional processing of sales invoices Larry's Landscaping & Garden Supply

Required

▶ *Access Invoice No. 129 for Tracy Stinson Customer: Job. In addition to the items already included on the invoice, add the following item to Invoice No. 129: 2 hours of Design (Custom landscape design).*

▶ *Process the revised invoice and save it.*

a. Explain how you prepared the revised sales invoice and provide the new total for the revised invoice.

_____

_____

_____

b. Assume there were errors in revised Invoice No. 129 and you want to void the transaction.

▶ *Void Invoice No. 129. If you receive a message about Cash Basis reports being affected, click OK.*

How is Invoice No. 129 included in the Invoices List?

_____

_____

_____

c. What is the amount due on Invoice No. 129 after you voided it?

_____

Internal Controls

P-3-4. Valid data controls for Larry's Landscaping & Garden Supply

Required

a. Explain what is meant by valid data controls and what are their purposes?

_____

_____

_____

b. Open the Enter Bills window and start recording a bill from Computer Services by DJ. Make up details for recording the transaction, including invalid data. Give two examples of the invalid data you attempted to enter and the resulting valid data control messages generated by *QuickBooks*.

_____

_____

_____

_____

_____

_____

_____

Name:

4 Obtaining Information

Chapter

As described on page v of this book, you should restore both Rock Castle Construction and Larry's Landscaping & Garden Supply using the initial backups that you downloaded from the Armond Dalton Resources website. Restore both companies before working on this chapter's question and problem material. If you cannot recall how to restore a backup, refer to the section "Restore Company Backup Files" in the E-materials located at www.armonddaltonresources.com.

PART I: QUESTIONS

Lists

Q-4-1. Larry's Landscaping & Garden Supply — Questions about customers, sales, and collections

Required

a. What is the dollar amount of the largest customer account balance on the current date (12/15/2022)?

_____

b. What was the total amount of customer invoices for this fiscal year-to-date (10/01/2022 to 12/15/2022)? *Hint:* Enter the proper time period in the Date box.

_____

c. What was the total dollar amount of open customer invoices as of 12/15/2022?

_____

d. How many customer payments were received via VISA this fiscal year-to-date (10/01/2022 to 12/15/2022)?

_____

Q-4-2. Larry's Landscaping & Garden Supply — Questions about payroll

Required

a. How many paychecks did Jenny Miller receive in the last calendar quarter (07/01/2022 to 09/30/2022)?

_____

b. Which employee received the largest net paycheck during the last month (November 2022)?

_____

Drill Down

Q-4-3. Larry's Landscaping & Garden Supply — Use drill down in cash receipts

Required

▶ *Open the Customer Center: Received Payments list window.*

▶ *Drill down on Check No. 1164 dated 11/11/2022.*

a. Who was the customer?

_____

b. What sales invoice number was paid with check #1164?

_____

c. Was there an early payment discount taken by the customer who paid with check #1164?

_____

Name:

Q-4-4. **Larry's Landscaping & Garden Supply—Use drill down of employees**

Required

▶ *Open the Employees Center and use drill down to open the Edit Employee window for Duncan Fisher.*

a. In what year was Duncan Fisher hired?

_____

b. What is Duncan Fisher's regular hourly pay rate?

_____

c. How many withholding allowances does Duncan Fisher have for federal income tax purposes?

_____

d. What was the amount of federal income tax withholding on Duncan Fisher's 10/22/2022 paycheck? *Hint:* You may need to change the Date box to This Calendar Quarter.

_____

e. How much did Larry's Landscaping & Garden Supply pay for Duncan Fisher's "Medicare Company" for the pay period covered by his 10/20/2022 paycheck?

_____

f. How much was the total year-to-date California withholding showing on Duncan Fisher's 10/20/2022 paycheck?

_____

Q-4-5. **Larry's Landscaping & Garden Supply—Use drill down of Chart of Accounts**

Required

a. Use drill down to determine the balance in the Accounts Payable account at 11/30/2022. What is the balance?

_____

b. What was the dollar amount for the debit posted to Accounts Payable on 11/01/2022?

_____

Custom Transaction Detail Reports

Q-4-6. **Larry's Landscaping & Garden Supply—Custom Transaction Detail Report for sales**

Management is considering eliminating an inventory item, 1/2" Vinyl Irrigation Line, because of low sales levels.

Required

What were the total dollar sales of the inventory item 1/2" Vinyl Irrigation Line last fiscal year (10/01/2021 to 09/30/2022)? *Hint:* Use Item for the Filter.

_____

PART II: PROBLEMS AND REPORTS/PRINTOUTS

Lists

P-4-1. Rock Castle Construction—Print a list of payroll checks

Required

Print a list of payroll checks for this calendar year-to-date (01/01/2022 to 12/15/2022) sorted by net pay from smallest to largest. The list should include the following columns from left to right: Employee, Date, Paid Through, and Amount. *Hint:* Use the Transactions tab in the Employee Center. Recall that you can sort by clicking on the appropriate column heading(s).

P-4-2. Rock Castle Construction—Print a list of vendor transactions and export the list

Required

Print a list of bills for the vendor Cal Gas & Electric for this fiscal year-to-date (01/01/2022 to 12/15/2022) using only four columns in the following order from left to right: Vendor, Type, Date, and Amount. *Hint:* Start with the Vendor Center and Vendors tab open so that you can segregate Cal Gas & Electric transactions.

Next, export the list to Excel using the Export Transactions menu item. After exporting to Excel, print a list of bills for Cal Gas & Electric. The columns should be the same as listed previously. All headings should be in bold. The printout should include a description of the printout and the date.

Custom Transaction Detail Reports

P-4-3. **Rock Castle Construction — Custom Transaction Detail Report for parts sales invoices**

Management wants a listing of all parts invoice transactions in November 2022 in excess of $300. *Hint:* You will need to use the Filters tab to segregate "All parts" items.

Required

Prepare and print the report.

Reports

P-4-4. **Rock Castle Construction — Print a profit & loss statement**

Required

a. Print and hand in a standard profit and loss statement for Rock Castle Construction for the last fiscal year (01/01/2021 to 12/31/2021) in two columns.

b. Print and hand in a standard profit and loss statement for Rock Castle Construction, by quarter, for the last fiscal year (01/01/2021 to 12/31/2021). Each quarter and the total should be in separate columns. Which quarter was the most profitable?

_____

_____

P-4-5. **Rock Castle Construction — Print a sales report and use drill down**

Required

a. Print and hand in the Sales by Customer Summary Report for Rock Castle Construction for the current fiscal quarter-to-date (10/01/2022–12/15/2022).

b. Using only drill down, access Invoice No. 1071 for Pretell Real Estate and print the sales invoice.

P-4-6. Rock Castle Construction—Print an inventory valuation summary

Required

a. Print and hand in the inventory valuation summary for Rock Castle Construction as of December 15, 2022.

b. Drill down on the Interior Wood Door (P-187055T) and then print the resulting inventory valuation detail as of December 15, 2022.

P-4-7. Larry's Landscaping & Garden Supply—Print a general ledger trial balance and export it to Excel

Required

a. Print and hand in the general ledger trial balance for Larry's Landscaping & Garden Supply as of 10/31/2022. Export the report to Excel and then delete all accounts except income statement accounts and retained earnings. Print and hand in the Excel report.

b. Print and hand in the general ledger trial balance for Larry's Landscaping & Garden Supply as of 10/31/2022 for income statement accounts only, but including retained earnings, using *QuickBooks* instead of exporting to Excel. *Hint:* Use modify Reports.

c. Print and hand in the general ledger trial balance as of 12/15/2022 for the following accounts: all cash accounts, all fixed asset accounts, all accumulated depreciation accounts, and all equity accounts. How did you accomplish generating and printing this report?

_____

_____

_____

_____

_____

6 Purchases and Cash Disbursements

Chapter

As described on page v of this book, you should restore both Rock Castle Construction and Larry's Landscaping & Garden Supply using the initial backups that you downloaded from the Armond Dalton Resources website. Restore both companies before working on this chapter's question and problem material. If you cannot recall how to restore a backup, refer to the section "Restore Company Backup Files" in the E-materials located at www.armonddaltonresources.com.

PART I: QUESTIONS

Purchases and Cash Disbursements Cycle

Q-6-1.   Rock Castle Construction—Purchase Orders

Required

a. How many purchase orders were processed in November 2022 (last month)?

_____

b. What was the amount of the largest purchase order for November 2022 (last month)?

_____

c. How many different products were ordered on the largest purchase order for November 2022 (last month)?

_____

d. For Purchase Order No. 6223, what was the per-unit cost of the item purchased?

_____

Q-6-2. Rock Castle Construction—Bills

Required

a. How many purchases did Rock Castle Construction make from 12/11/2022 to 12/15/2022 (this week-to-date) through the Bills process? (Do not include credits.)

_____

b. What is the amount of the largest purchase from 12/11/2022 to 12/15/2022 (this week-to-date) through the Bills process?

_____

c. What service was purchased on Invoice No. 20001 on 12/12/2022 from Lew Plumbing?

_____

d. What is the total amount of purchases through the Bills process so far in this fiscal year-to-date (01/01/2022–12/15/2022), net of credits?

_____

e. What is the largest open vendor invoice amount due other than 0 at 12/15/2022 (this fiscal year-to-date)?

_____

f. What general ledger account is credited when Bills are entered?

_____

Q-6-3. Rock Castle Construction—Cash Disbursements

Required

a. Which account is debited when a transaction is processed using the Pay Bills window in *QuickBooks*?

_____

b. Which account is credited when a transaction is processed using the Write Checks Window?

_____

c. What was the total of cash disbursements through Bill Payments for this fiscal year-to-date (01/01/2022 to 12/15/2022)?

_____

d. How many invoices were paid with Check No. 473?

_____

e. How many cash disbursement transactions in the last fiscal quarter (07/01/2022 to 09/30/2022) were recorded without having been previously recorded as an accounts payable? Do not include checks with 0 amounts (voided checks). *Hint:* Use the Checks option instead of the Bill Payments option in the Transactions tab of the Vendor Center.

_____

f. Which account was debited for Check No. 402?

_____

Q-6-4. Rock Castle Construction — Bill Payments

Required

Answer the following questions about Check No. 461 written on 11/21/2022 to Timberloft Lumber (in Bill Payments).

a. How many invoices were paid with Check No. 461?

_____

b. What were the discount terms of the invoice(s) paid with Check No. 461? *Hint:* After drilling down to the Bill Payments window for Check No. 461, use the Reports tab → Transaction History option to drill down on the related invoice(s).

_____

c. Did Rock Castle Construction take the discount on the invoice(s) paid with Check No. 461? *Hint:* After drilling down to the Bill Payments window for Check No. 461, use the Reports tab → Transaction History option to drill down to the related invoice(s).

_____

Q-6-5. Rock Castle Construction — Accounts Payable

Required

a. What was the total accounts payable on 11/30/2022?

_____

b. Which vendor had the largest outstanding balance on 11/30/2022?

_____

Q-6-6. Rock Castle Construction — Accounting transactions resulting from processing purchasing and cash disbursement transactions

Required

For each of the following transactions, select the proper accounting entry from the list provided.

a. Inventory was received but not paid for on a purchase order. Payment terms were 2% 10, Net 30.

1. DR A/C #12100 Inventory Asset
   CR A/C #50100 Cost of Goods Sold

2. DR A/C #12100 Inventory Asset
   CR A/C #20000 Accounts Payable

3. DR A/C #50100 Cost of Goods Sold
   CR A/C #20000 Accounts Payable

4. DR A/C #12100 Inventory Asset
   CR A/C #54300 Job Materials

5. None of the above

b. A purchase order for the purchase of inventory was prepared and saved.

1. DR A/C #12100 Inventory Asset
   CR A/C #50100 Cost of Goods Sold

2. DR A/C #12100 Inventory Asset
   CR A/C #20000 Accounts Payable

3. DR A/C #50100 Cost of Goods Sold
   CR A/C #20000 Accounts Payable

4. DR A/C #50100 Cost of Goods Sold
   CR A/C #12100 Inventory Asset

5. None of the above (no accounting entry necessary)

c. The inventory received on a purchase order was paid for within 20 days of the purchase. Payment terms on invoice were 2% 10, Net 30.

    1. DR A/C #20000 Accounts Payable
          CR A/C #10100 Checking
          CR A/C #54599 Less Discounts Taken

    2. DR A/C #20000 Accounts Payable
          CR A/C #50100 Cost of Goods Sold

    3. DR A/C # 20000 Accounts Payable
          CR A/C #10100 Checking

    4. DR A/C #50100 Cost of Goods Sold
          CR A/C #10100 Checking

    5. None of the above

d. An invoice was received and processed, but not paid for from Cal Gas & Electric.

    1. DR A/C #65100 Utilities
          CR A/C #10100 Checking

    2. DR A/C #65100 Utilities
          CR A/C #54300 Job Materials

    3. DR A/C #65100 Utilities
          CR A/C #20600 CalOil Credit Card

    4. DR A/C #65100 Utilities
          CR A/C #20000 Accounts Payable

    5. None of the above

e. The monthly payment to Bank of Anycity for its notes payable was paid.

    1. DR A/C #62400 Interest Expense
          CR A/C # 10100 Checking

    2. DR A/C #28700 Note Payable - Bank of Anycity
          CR A/C #10100 Checking

    3. DR A/C #62400 Interest Expense
      DR A/C #28700 Note Payable, Bank of Anycity
          CR A/C #10100 Checking

    4. DR A/C #20000 Accounts Payable
          CR A/C #10100 Checking

    5. None of the above

f. The invoice for accounting and tax services from Fay, Maureen Lynn, CPA was received and paid for.

   1. DR A/C #63600 Professional Fees
       CR A/C #10100 Checking

   2. DR A/C #10100 Checking
       CR A/C #20000 Accounts Payable

   3. DR A/C #54300 Job Expenses
       CR A/C #10100 Checking

   4. DR A/C #63600 – Professional Fees
       CR A/C #54300 Job Expenses

   5. None of the above

Q-6-7. Rock Castle Construction—Subsidiary account balances affected by processing purchasing and cash disbursement transactions

Required

For each of the following transactions, choose the subsidiary record or records affected by the transaction and the effect on each (increase or decrease) from the list provided.

a. Inventory was received but not paid for on a purchase order. Payment terms were 2% 10, Net 30.

   1. Inventory decrease, Accounts Payable decrease

   2. Inventory decrease, Accounts Payable increase

   3. Inventory increase, Accounts Payable increase

   4. Inventory increase, Accounts Payable decrease

   5. None of the above

b. A purchase order for the purchase of inventory was prepared and saved.

1. Inventory decrease, Accounts Payable decrease

2. Inventory decrease, Accounts Payable increase

3. Inventory increase, Accounts Payable decrease

4. Inventory increase, Accounts Receivable decrease

5. No subsidiary records are affected

c. The inventory received on a purchase order was paid for within 20 days of the purchase. Payment terms on invoice were 2% 10, Net 30.

1. Inventory decrease, Accounts Payable decrease

2. Inventory increase, Accounts Payable decrease

3. Accounts Payable decrease only

4. Accounts Payable increase only

5. None of the above

d. An invoice was received and processed, but not paid for from Cal Gas & Electric.

1. Accounts Payable increase only

2. Accounts Payable decrease only

3. Accounts Payable increase, Inventory increase

4. Accounts Payable increase, Inventory decrease

5. None of the above

e. The monthly payment to Bank of Anycity for its notes payable was paid.

1. Accounts Payable decrease only

2. Accounts Payable increase only

3. Accounts Receivable decrease only

4. Accounts Receivable increase only

5. No subsidiary records are affected

PART II – PROBLEMS AND REPORTS/PRINTOUTS

P-6-1. Larry's Landscaping & Garden Supply — Vendors

Management wants a list of vendors with account balances as of 12/15/2022, sorted from the smallest to the largest amount outstanding. The following columns are to be included, from left to right: Active Status, Name (Vendor), Balance Total, Vendor Type, and Terms. *Hint:* Use the Vendor tab of the Vendor Center. Then change the view to include only vendors with open balances prior to sorting and printing.

Required

Prepare and print the list requested by management (called the Vendor List in *QuickBooks*).

P-6-2. Larry's Landscaping & Garden Supply — Purchases, disbursements, and accounts payable

Required

You know that beginning accounts payable, plus purchases on account, minus purchases returns and allowances, minus payments on account equals ending accounts payable. Show that reconciliation by using the information available in *QuickBooks* for December 15, 2022, and beginning (November 30, 2022) and ending (December 15, 2022) accounts payable.

_____

_____

_____

_____

_____

_____

P-6-3. Larry's Landscaping & Garden Supply—Purchases

The management of Larry's Landscaping & Garden Supply wants a listing of all purchases in excess of $250 for this fiscal quarter-to-date (10/01/2022 to 12/15/2022). The listing is to be sorted by purchase invoice total from largest to smallest amount and is to include only the following four columns in the order listed, from left to right: Vendor Name, Invoice Total, Outstanding Balance at 12/15/2022, and Invoice Date. The listing should include a total of the invoice amounts.

Required

Prepare and print the list in the format requested by management. Export to Excel if it is necessary to prepare the report. Rename the columns after exporting to Excel, if necessary.

P-6-4. Larry's Landscaping & Garden Supply—Internal control questions

Required

a. Many vendors' names cannot be deleted on 12/15/2022. Why will *QuickBooks* not allow you to delete the accounts?

_____

_____

_____

_____

b. Duncan Fisher is responsible for processing all purchase invoices. Explain why he is likely to need access to accounts payable maintenance. Explain why it is desirable to deny access to him for processing cash disbursement transactions.

_____

_____

_____

_____

c. Duncan Fisher has accessed the Enter Bills window to process a purchase transaction for Middlefield Nursery. List five types of information (such as Vendor) that can be accessed in the window by clicking on an icon or drop-down list arrow (to reduce typing the information and thereby saving time and reducing the likelihood of errors):

1. _____

2. _____

3. _____

4. _____

5. _____

d. Duncan Fisher has entered all information needed to process a vendor's invoice for Middlefield Nursery in the Enter Bills window and has clicked the Save and Close button to process the transaction. List five types of information that are automatically prepared or updated as a result of the activity. Example: Vendor Balance: total list in the Vendor Center for Middlefield Nursery is updated.

1. _____

2. _____

3. _____

4. _____

5. _____

e. Duncan Fisher has accessed the Enter Bills window to process a purchase transaction for Middlefield Nursery. List three pieces of information that are automatically displayed after Duncan has clicked on Middlefield Nursery in the Vendor box.

1. _____

2. _____

3. _____

P-6-5. Larry's Landscaping & Garden Supply — Processing transactions

Required

The following are situations where an error or fraud has occurred. You are to recommend one or more internal controls to prevent or detect the error or fraud.

a. Jenny Miller processed a nonexistent purchase transaction payable to herself. She then processed a check to pay for the purchase and forged the controller's signature.

_____

_____

_____

_____

_____

_____

b. Duncan Fisher, the employee responsible for processing purchases, started a fictitious company and processed a purchase transaction for that company. The cash disbursements processor processed the check to pay the invoice and the controller signed the check and mailed it to the fictitious company.

_____

_____

_____

_____

_____

c. When Duncan Fisher established a new vendor in Maintain Vendors he entered the wrong default account for inventory. Every inventory purchase transaction with that vendor was processed using that wrong account.

_____

_____

_____

_____

_____

Name:

P-6-6.   Larry's Landscaping & Garden Supply—Processing transactions

You are to do the maintenance and process the transactions that follow in the purchases and cash disbursements cycle for Larry's Landscaping & Garden Supply. The company has decided to add a limited line of outdoor furniture and accessories to their inventory to sell as retail to existing customers. They will start by buying two inventory items for resale: fire pits and umbrellas.

Required

a. First you will do the required maintenance and then you will prepare a purchase order for the company's first purchase of these items from Conner Garden Supplies.

▶ *Do the maintenance required to set up the two inventory items using the information that follows:*

		Fire Pits	**Umbrellas**
■	Type:	Inventory Part	Inventory Part
■	Type Name:	Fire pit	Umbrella
■	Description:	Fire pit	Umbrella
■	Cost:	$114.00	$89.00
■	Sales Price:	$197.00	$165.00
■	COGS Account:	Cost of Goods Sold	Cost of Goods Sold
■	Tax Code:	Tax	Tax
■	Preferred Vendor:	Conner Garden Supplies	Conner Garden Supplies
■	Income Account:	Retail Sales	Retail Sales
■	Asset Account:	Inventory Asset	Inventory Asset
■	Reorder Point:	10	15

A purchase order was sent to Conner Garden Supplies for the purchase of fire pits and umbrellas. Information about the purchase order and inventory follows.

► Process the purchase order using the information that follows, print it, and save it.

	Vendor:	Conner Garden Supplies
■	Date:	December 19, 2022
■	PO Number:	6238
■	Inventory items ordered:	

Item	Description	Quantity	Unit Cost
Fire Pit	Fire Pit	25	$114.00
Umbrella	Umbrella	35	89.00

b. The fire pits and umbrellas ordered on Purchase Order No. 6238 were delivered December 21, 2022. Conner Garden Supplies delivered all of the fire pits, but only 20 umbrellas. They included Invoice No. 4134 in the amount of $4,630.00. No payment was made.

► *Process the receipt of the inventory using the information provided, print the bill, and then save the transaction.*

c. On December 22, 2022, Larry's Landscaping & Garden Supply paid for the full amount due on Invoice No. 4134 to Conner Garden Supplies.

► *Process the payment of the invoice using the information provided.*

► *Print the check and also save the transaction.*

d. On December 26, 2022, Larry's Landscaping & Garden Supply determined that 4 of the fire pits on Invoice No. 4134 were not of the quality that had been agreed upon. Conner Garden Supplies agreed to pick up the fire pits and give Larry's Landscaping & Garden Supply full credit. Conner Garden Supplies issued Credit Memo No. 72191 (processed as a debit memo by Larry's Landscaping & Garden Supply) on December 26, 2022, for the return.

► *Process the debit memo (vendor credit memo) using the information provided.*

► *Print the debit memo (vendor credit memo) and also save the transaction.*

7 Sales and Cash Receipts
Chapter

As described on page v of this book, you should restore both Rock Castle Construction and Larry's Landscaping & Garden Supply using the initial backups that you downloaded from the Armond Dalton Resources website. Restore both companies before working on this chapter's questions and problem material. If you cannot recall how to restore a backup, refer to the section "Restore Company Backup Files" in the E-materials located at www.armonddaltonresources.com.

PART I - QUESTIONS

Q-7-1.   Larry's Landscaping & Garden Supply — Credit Sales

Required

a. How many credit sales invoices were processed in November 2022. Do not include items with "FC" in the Num column; those are finance charges.

_____

b. What is the amount of the largest credit sale invoice (dollar amount) for November 2022?

_____

c. What was sold on the smallest credit sale invoice (dollar amount) for November 2022?

_____

d. What is the lowest credit sale invoice number (document number) for November 2022?

_____

e. What was the nature of the service provided to David Hughes on Invoice No. 104?

_____

f. Which general ledger account is debited for the sale of inventory on credit?

    1. Inventory Asset

    2. Checking

    3. Accounts Receivable

    4. Job Materials

    5. Sales

g. Which subsidiary account/accounts is/are affected by sale of inventory on credit and how is each affected?

    1. Inventory increase, Accounts Receivable decrease

    2. Inventory increase only

    3. Accounts Receivable increase only

    4. Inventory decrease, Accounts Receivable increase

    5. None of the above

Q-7-2. Larry's Landscaping & Garden Supply—Collection of Accounts Receivable

Required

a. How many sales invoices were collected using a customer's VISA credit card during the last fiscal year (10/01/2021 to 09/30/2022)?

_____

b. What was the amount of the largest account receivable collection during the last fiscal year (10/01/2021 to 09/30/2022) (including both checks and credit card receipts)?

_____

c. For Receipt No. 1094 on 08/28/2022, what was the amount of the sales tax on the original invoice? *Hint:* Use the Reports tab, Transaction History option from the Customer Payment window to drill down to the original invoice.

_____

d. Which subsidiary account or accounts are affected when accounts receivable are collected?

1. Accounts Receivable and Inventory Asset
2. Inventory Asset
3. Accounts Receivable
4. Accounts Payable
5. None of the above

Q-7-3.   Larry's Landscaping & Garden Supply—Accounts Receivable

Required

a. What is the name of the customer with the second largest receivables balance at 12/15/2022?

_____

b. How many customers have a balance outstanding in excess of $1,500 at 12/15/2022?

_____

c. What are the payment terms for Edward Blackwell?

_____

Q-7-4.   Larry's Landscaping & Garden Supply — Cash Sales

Required

a. How many cash sales were processed this fiscal quarter-to-date (10/01/2022 to 12/15/2022), including those paid for by credit card?

_____

b. What was sold on the smallest cash sale for this fiscal quarter-to-date (10/01/2022 to 12/15/2022)?

_____

c. Why was there no sales tax on cash sale Invoice No. 11 on 10/26/2022?

1. The invoice total was under the sales tax threshold.
2. Invoice No. 11 was for services performed.
3. Invoice No. 11 was for both inventory and services performed.
4. N/A – there was sales tax included on Invoice No. 11.
5. None of the above

d. Which general ledger account(s) was(were) credited for the cash sale to Natalie Chapman on Invoice No. 13? *Hint:* Use the Transactions Journal button in the Reports tab.

_____

e. Were any subsidiary accounts affected by the cash sale to Natalie Chapman on Invoice No. 13? *Hint:* Use the Transactions Journal button in the Report tab to first determine which general ledger accounts were affected by the cash sale. Based on the general ledger accounts that were affected, determine whether any subsidiary accounts would have also been affected.

_____

Q-7-5. Rock Castle Construction — Sale of Inventory, Return, and Collection

Required

a. Which of the following includes the correct Home Page icon, document printed, transaction listing in the Customer Center affected, and master file(s) affected by the sale of inventory to a customer on account (credit sale)?

1. Create Invoices (Home Page icon); Credit Memo (document printed); Invoices (transaction listing affected); Accounts Receivable (master file affected).

2. Create Invoices (Home Page icon); Invoice (document printed); Received Payments (transaction listing affected); Accounts Receivable and Inventory (master files affected).

3. Receive Payments (Home Page icon); Invoice (document printed); Invoices (transaction listing affected); Accounts Receivable and Inventory (master files affected).

4. Create Invoices (Home Page icon); Invoice (document printed); Invoices (transaction listing affected); Accounts Receivable and Inventory (master files affected).

5. None of the above

b. Which of the following includes the correct Home Page icon, document printed, transaction listing in the Customer Center affected, and master file(s) affected by the return of goods by a customer who previously purchased the goods through a credit sale?

    1. Refunds & Credits (Home Page icon); Credit Memo (document printed); Invoices (transaction listing affected); Accounts Receivable (master file affected).

    2. Refunds & Credits (Home Page icon); Credit Memo (document printed); Credit Memos (transaction listing affected); Accounts Receivable and Inventory (master files affected).

    3. Refunds & Credits (Home Page icon); Credit Memo (document printed); Credit Memos (transaction listing affected); Accounts Receivable (master file affected).

    4. Create Invoices (Home Page icon); Credit Memo (document printed); Invoices (transaction listing affected); Accounts Receivable and Inventory (master files affected).

    5. None of the above

c. Which of the following includes the correct Home Page icon, document printed, transaction listing in the Customer Center affected, and master file(s) affected by the collection of an account receivable?

    1. Receive Payments (Home Page icon); Payment Receipt (document printed); Received Payments (transaction listing affected); Accounts Receivable (master file affected).

    2. Receive Payments (Home Page icon); Payment Receipt (document printed); Received Payments (transaction listing affected); Accounts Receivable and Inventory (master files affected)

    3. Receive Payments (Home Page icon); Invoice (document printed); Received Payments (transaction listing affected); Accounts Receivable (master file affected).

    4. Refunds & Credits (Home Page icon); Payment Receipt (document printed); Received Payments (transaction listing affected); Accounts Receivable (master file affected).

    5. None of the above

Name:

Q-7-6. Rock Castle Construction — Credit Memos

Required

a. How many credit memos were processed for this fiscal year-to-date (01/01/2022 to 12/15/2022)?

_____

b. Which of the following best describes the reason that Credit Memo No. 4002 was processed?

1. Damaged goods were returned.
2. Customer was billed for the incorrect number of inventory items.
3. Customer was charged the wrong price for the inventory items purchased.
4. Customer decided not to keep the goods.
5. None of the above

c. What was the check number issued for the refund on Credit Memo No. 4002? *Hint:* Use the Transaction tab on the right side of the Create Credit Memos/Refunds window to locate the information.

_____

PART II – PROBLEMS AND REPORTS/PRINTOUTS

P-7-1.   Rock Castle Construction—Sales

The management of Rock Castle Construction wants listings of sales invoices for the most recent quarter to date in 2022 (10/01/2022 to 12/15/22). The listing is to be sorted by sales invoice total from smallest to largest amount and is to include only the following six columns in the order listed, from left to right: Num, Customer, Amount, Date, Terms, and Due Date. Do not export to Excel. *Hint:* Use Customize Transaction List Columns.

Required

Prepare and print a list of the sales invoices in the format requested by management. Why are the terms for several customers not included in the Terms column? *Note:* In each case the invoice showed a due date the same as the invoice date.

_____

_____

_____

_____

_____

_____

P-7-2. Rock Castle Construction—Collections on Accounts Receivable

The management of Rock Castle Construction wants a listing of collections on accounts receivable (Received Payments) in excess of $5,000 for last year (01/01/2021 to 12/31/2021). The listing is to be sorted by invoice date from earliest to latest and is to include only the following three columns in the order listed, from left to right: Customer, Collection Amount, and Collection Date. The total of collections on the listing should be included. The schedule should have proper headings and your name. Export the information to Excel to complete the requirement. You may need to edit some of the column headings after exporting to Excel.

Required

Prepare and print a list of the cash receipts from collections on accounts receivable in the format requested by management.

P-7-3. Rock Castle Construction—Customer Statements

The management of Rock Castle Construction wants customer statements prepared and printed for three customers at November 30, 2022. Robert Allard, Doug Jacobson, and Mackey's Nursery and Garden Supply. The statement period should be from November 1, 2022, to November 30, 2022. *Hint:* Choose at the customer level, not the job level.

Required

Set the defaults for preparing statements using the criteria requested by management. Print the customer statements.

P-7-4. Rock Castle Construction—Customer Collections

The management of Rock Castle Construction wants an analysis of the Pretell Real Estate's customer account at November 30, 2022. Identify which sales invoices are still unpaid as of year-end.

Required

Prepare a report of these invoices with the following columns in the heading from left to right: Date, Invoice Number, Invoice Amount, and Amount Unpaid (Open Balance). Include totals for the Invoice Amount and Amount Unpaid columns and a heading showing the company name, a description of the report, the name of the customer, and the date. *Hint:* Use the Display tab in the Modify Report: Open Invoices window to customize the report to include the necessary columns.

Name:

P-7-5.   Rock Castle Construction—Internal Control

Required

a. Open the Customers & Jobs tab in the Customer Center. Attempt to delete the accounts receivable Room Addition account for Jason Burch (Delete Customer: Job). What is the message on the window after you answer that you want to delete it? Why does that control exist?

_____

_____

_____

_____

b. Elizabeth Mason is responsible for processing all sales invoices. Explain why she is likely to need access to accounts receivable maintenance.

_____

_____

_____

_____

c. Explain why it is desirable to deny Elizabeth Mason access to processing cash receipt transactions, processing credit memos, and processing general journal transactions.

_____

_____

_____

_____

d. Elizabeth Mason has entered all information needed to process a sales invoice for Ecker Designs and has clicked the Save button in the Create Invoices–Accounts Receivable window. List seven types of information that are automatically prepared or updated as a result of the activity.

Note: There are many items in reports including those in Company & Financial, Customers & Receivables, Sales, and Accountant & Taxes.

   1. **Example:** Customer Balance—detail file for Ecker Designs is updated

   2. _____

   3._____

   4. _____

   5._____

   6. _____

   7._____

e. Elizabeth Mason has accessed the Create Invoices–Accounts Receivable window to process a sales invoice for Aaron Davies. List six types of information that can be accessed in the window by clicking on an icon or drop-down arrow to eliminate typing the information and thereby saving time and reducing the likelihood of errors.

   1. **Example:** Customer: Job

   2. _____

   3._____

   4. _____

   5._____

   6. _____

Name:

8 Chapter | Payroll and Other Activities

As described on page v of this book, you should restore both Rock Castle Construction and Larry's Landscaping & Garden Supply using the initial backups that you downloaded from the Armond Dalton Resources website. Restore both companies before working on this chapter's questions and problem material. If you cannot recall how to restore a backup, refer to the section "Restore Company Backup Files" in the E-materials located at www.armonddaltonresources.com.

PART I - QUESTIONS

Q-8-1.   Rock Castle Construction—Employees

Required

a. How many employees does Rock Castle Construction currently have in its master file?

_____

b. What date was Elizabeth Mason hired?

_____

c. What is Elizabeth Mason's home address?

_____

_____

Q-8-2. Rock Castle Construction—Payroll

Required

a. For the employee Elizabeth Mason, what is the total federal withholding amount for the current calendar year-to-date per Check No. 10077 (01/01/2022–12/15/2022)?

_____

b. What type of employee is Elizabeth Mason, salaried or hourly?

_____

Q-8-3. Rock Castle Construction—Monthly payroll summary

Required

a. What were Gregg Schneider's total regular hours for the two paychecks issued in the month of October 2022?

_____

b. What were Gregg Schneider's total overtime hours for the two paychecks issued in the month of October 2022?

_____

c. What was Gregg Schneider's total gross pay for the two paychecks issued in the month of October 2022?

_____

d. What was Gregg Schneider's total federal withholding for the two paychecks issued in the month of October 2022?

_____

Q-8-4. Rock Castle Construction Company—General journal entries

Required

a. How many general journal entries did Rock Castle Construction Company make last fiscal year (01/01/2021 to 12/31/2021)?

_____

b. How often does Rock Castle Construction record depreciation expense? *Hint:* Examine the general journal entries for last fiscal year.

_____

Q-8-5. Rock Castle Construction—Possible general journal entries

Required

A new accountant prepared the following general journal entries on February 28, 2022, for Rock Castle Construction. Each of these general journal entries includes an error. Choose the best explanation of each error from the choices provided.

a. 60600   Bank Service Charges $ 175
     10100   Checking $ 157
                    Bank service charge for February

1. The bank service charge expense should have been credited, not debited.

2. The checking account should have been debited, not credited.

3. The total debits do not equal the total credits.

4. All of the above

5. None of the above

b.

12000	Inventory	$ 8,575	
10100	Checking		$ 8,575
	Purchase of inventory		

1. Inventory should have been credited, not debited.

2. The account # for inventory is incorrect; should be 12100

3. The checking account should have been debited, not credited.

4. The Inventory account should never be adjusted by a general journal entry.

5. None of the above

c.

17000	Accumulated Depreciation	$ 1,250	
60900	Depreciation Expense		$ 1,250
	Depreciation for February		

1. Depreciation should be recorded annually, not monthly.

2. The accountant should never make an entry directly to accumulated depreciation.

3. Accumulated depreciation should have been credited, not debited.

4. Depreciation expense should have been debited, not credited.

5. Both 3 and 4 are correct.

d.

50100	Cost of Goods Sold	$ 5,500	
12100	Inventory		$ 5,500
	Adjust inventory for differences between the master files and the actual inventory		

1. Inventory should have been debited, not credited.

2. The wrong account number was used for cost of goods sold.

3. Inventory adjustments should be made using the Adjust Quantity/Value on Hand window in *QuickBooks*, not using a general journal entry.

4. All of the above are correct statements.

5. None of the above are correct statements.

Q-8-6. Rock Castle Construction—Bank reconciliation questions

Required

a. Which of the following statements best describes the purpose of a bank reconciliation?

1. A bank reconciliation is required in order to properly record all cash receipts and cash disbursements of a company.

2. A bank reconciliation is required by the bank.

3. A bank reconciliation reconciles the balance per general ledger with the balance reported by the bank, taking into account deposits in transit, outstanding checks, and bank service charges.

4. A bank reconciliation is required by generally accepted auditing standards.

5. All of the above equally describe the purpose of a bank reconciliation.

b. For good internal control, how often should bank reconciliations be prepared?

1. Daily

2. Weekly

3. Monthly

4. Quarterly

5. Annually

PART II – PROBLEMS AND REPORTS/PRINTOUTS

P-8-1.   Rock Castle Construction —Payroll Maintenance

Required

a. Perform maintenance for a new hourly employee, Samantha Bengel, that Rock Castle Construction hired on 12/20/2022 using the information that follows. Take screenshots of the main tabs in the New Employee window and print/save the screenshots to be handed in to your instructor.

Personal tab
- Name: Samantha Bengel
- Social Security Number: 465-48-6697

Address & Contact tab
- Address: 6117 Green Road
                                             Bayshore, CA 94326
- Telephone (Main Phone):   555-7298

Employment Info tab
- Hire Date: 12/20/2022
- Employment Details Type: Regular

Payroll Info tab
- Regular Pay: $28 per hour
- Overtime Rate: $42 per hour
- Payroll Schedule: Biweekly
- Class:
- Health Insurance Amount: – $155.00

Taxes button

Federal tab
- Filing Status: Married (two incomes)
- Allowances: 2

State tab
- State: CA
- Allowances: 2

---

b. Dan Miller has requested that his federal withholdings allowances be increased to 4, with no change in the others. Elizabeth Mason has moved and her new address is 1555 Chilson Rd., Middlefield, CA 93242. She has also requested a change in her filing status as of this pay period from single to married, and her allowance to 2 for all withholdings. Make these changes. Take screenshots of the relevant tabs in each employee's Edit Employee window and print/save the screenshots to be handed in to your instructor.

P-8-2.   Rock Castle Construction—General journal entries

At the end of every quarter, Rock Castle Construction's controller makes several general journal entries. In this problem, you will prepare and print general journal entries for the third quarter of the current fiscal year. Be sure to print each general journal entry before moving to the next one.

a. Rock Castle Construction started accruing the interest expense on its mortgage on a monthly basis, starting with the third quarter of the current fiscal year. Prepare and print a general journal entry dated 09/30/2022 to accrue the third quarter's interest expense on the mortgage payable. The quarterly interest expense incurred on the mortgage payable is $2,500. You will need to set up a new account on the fly for accrued interest. It will be an other current liability account and the account number will be #20300. The expense account is for Loan Interest is #62420.

b. The controller discovered that $445.79 of equipment repairs were mistakenly recorded in tools and machinery expense. Prepare and print a general journal entry dated 09/30/2022 to correct the misclassification. Use accounts #64230 and #64800 for your general journal entry.

c. The office manager discovered that the security deposit account #18700 includes $250 of prior years' security deposits that will not be able to be recovered from subcontractors. Prepare a general journal entry dated 09/30/2022 to remove the $250 from the security deposit account. Due to the small amount, the controller has decided to write off the $250 amount to the current year's activity in account #54500: Job Expenses – Subcontractors. Prepare and print the general journal entry.

Name:

P-8-3. Larry's Landscaping & Garden Supply—Inventory maintenance

The management of Larry's Landscaping & Garden Supply has decided to discontinue providing the inventory item "Irrigation Hose - 1/4" Line" and has requested that all maintenance dealing with this item be deleted. The company has also decided to increase the selling price of all service, inventory, and non-inventory items that have a selling price of more than $15 and less than $125 by $5.

Required

a. Try to delete the inventory item as instructed by management. Why can't you? When will you be able to delete the item?

_____

_____

_____

_____

b. Change the price of the items as instructed by management and print an item price list report that reflects the changes.

c. What will you do with a deleted inventory or non-inventory item if management later decides to begin providing the inventory item "Irrigation Hose = 1/4" Line" again?

_____

_____

_____

_____

P-8-4. Larry's Landscaping & Garden Supply — Adjusting inventory

There have been minimal sales of both rock fountains and fountain pumps this fiscal year. Rock fountains are not carried in inventory, but the quantity in the master file for fountain pumps is overstated. Management believes that there have been thefts and therefore requested that a count be made at 12/15/2022. The count showed 35 in current inventory. Management requests that a new account be set up for any necessary adjustment to the expense account "Inventory Shortage." Choose the account type "Cost of Goods Sold."

Required

a. Set up the new account, Inventory Shortage, "on the fly." Next, adjust the perpetual records of inventory to reflect the actual count, following management's instructions. Print the revised Item List. Include only the following three columns in the order listed from left to right: Description, Price, and Quantity on Hand. The report should include the company name, a description of the report, date, column headings, and the information requested.

b. Print a standard income statement for November 1 to December 15, 2022. The income statement should include the effects of the inventory adjustment made in part a.

c. Suggest an internal control to reduce the likelihood of theft of the inventory.

_____ _____

_____

_____

_____

_____

P-8-5. Larry's Landscaping & Garden Supply — Inventory dollar balances

QuickBooks maintains balances of inventory quantities in the inventory Item List, but not dollar amounts. Management wants to be sure the quantities in the Item List are consistent with the general ledger if the inventory items were extended.

Required

Use a different method to determine the total cost of each item in inventory and the total cost of all inventory items included in the inventory master file at 12/15/2022. Compare the cost you arrived at to the balance in the general ledger at 12/15/2022. What are the respective amounts? Which amount is correct?

_____

_____

_____

_____

_____

_____

_____

P-8-6. Rock Castle Construction — Bank reconciliation problem

Management requests that you prepare an interim bank reconciliation of the regular bank account as of December 15, 2022, for Rock Castle Construction. You have obtained all of the information online that you will need in order to do the bank reconciliation. The following information is provided for the bank reconciliation. Recall that at the beginning of the problem material in this chapter, you were reminded to restore the Rock Castle Construction dataset using the initial backup as described in the E-materials that you downloaded from the Armond Dalton Resources website. This problem assumes you have restored the initial backup, so if you have not done that yet you should do it now. (See the following page.)

Name:

Balance per bank online 12/15/2022:		$ 32,468.60

Outstanding checks as of 12/15/2022:

Check No.	Amount
472	656.23
488	2,142.78
501	625.00
502	640.92
503	754.50
505	45.00
507	1,358.00
509	450.00
511	696.52
512	400.00
516	1,629.27
10074	907.92
10076	1,350.15
	$ 11,656.29

Deposits in transit as of 12/15/2022:

Deposit Date	Amount
12/12/2022	$ 4,936.12
12/15/2022	7,633.28
12/15/2022	13,560.39
	$ 26,129.79

December bank service charge already debited to account by bank (A/C No. 60600):	$ 27.00

Required

Prepare an interim bank reconciliation as of December 15, 2022, for the regular checking account using the preceding information. Print and hand in the reconciliation after you have completed it.

Name:

Waren Sports Supply

PART I - QUESTIONS

Q-9-1. Accrued Interest Payable

Required

Interest accruals are calculated using a 365-day year with the day after the note was made counting as the first day. General ledger account numbers for the journal entry are: A/C #40800 (Interest Expense) and A/C #20900 (Interest Payable). Show your calculation below.

_____

_____

_____

Q-9-2. Bad Debt Expense and Allowance

Required

Bad debt expense is estimated once annually at the end of each year as 1/5 of one percent (0.0020) of net sales and is recorded in the general journal as of December 31. The "allowance" method of recording bad debt expense is used. General ledger account numbers for the journal entry are: A/C #40900 (Bad Debt Expense) and A/C #10300 (Allowance for Doubtful Account). Show your calculation below.

_____

_____

_____

Q-9-3. Federal Income Taxes

Required

The table below shows the corporate income tax rates for 2017:

U.S. Corporate Income Tax Table			
Pre-tax net income over –	But not over –	Tax is	Of the amount over –
$0	$50,000	15%	$0
50,000	75,000	$ 7,500 + 25%	50,000
75,000	100,000	13,750 + 34%	75,000
100,000	335,000	22,250 + 39%	100,000
335,000	10,000,000	$113,900 + 34%	335,000
10,000,000	15,000,000	3,400,000 + 35%	10,000,000
15,000,000	18,333,333	5,150,000 + 38%	15,000,000
18,333,333	.....	35%	0

General ledger account numbers for the journal entry are: A/C #40700 (Federal Income Tax Expense) and A/C #20700 (Federal Income Taxes Payable). Show your calculation below.

PART II - REPORTS/PRINTOUTS

Required

▶ *Print the following reports for Waren Sports Supply.*

Each of these reports has already been set up in the Memorized tab of the Report Center. This same list is provided at the end of Chapter 9, but it is included here for your convenience. All reports should be handed in to your instructor.

- 12/31/17 balance sheet
- 2017 income statement
- General journal for December 2017
- Accounts receivable aged trial balance as of 12/31/17
- Accounts payable aged trial balance as of 12/31/17
- Inventory valuation summary as of 12/31/17
- Employee earnings register for December 2017
- Sales journal for December 2017
- Cash receipts journal for December 2017
- Purchases journal for December 2017
- Cash disbursements journal for December 2017
- Payroll journal for December 2017
- December 2017 bank reconciliation
- Customer monthly statement for Eastern Wisconsin University
- Trial balance after year-end adjustments

Name:

10 New Company Setup
Chapter

As described on page v of this book, you should restore both Rock Castle Construction and Larry's Landscaping & Garden Supply using the initial backups that you downloaded from the Armond Dalton Resources website. Restore both companies before working on this chapter's problem material. If you cannot recall how to restore a backup, refer to the section "Restore Company Backup Files" in the E-materials located at www.armonddaltonresources.com.

PART I – QUESTIONS

Q-10-1. Rock Castle Construction — Setup of company information

Required

a. What is the Federal Employer ID for Rock Castle Construction? *Hint:* Start with the Menu Bar to find the information.

_____

b. Which window would you use to change the Federal Employer ID for Rock Castle Construction? *Hint:* Start with the Menu Bar to find the information.

_____

_____

Q-10-2. Rock Castle Construction—Changing information for a vendor

Required

Assume you entered the wrong address information for a vendor and did not discover it until after you had completed all setup procedures. Which of the following items would not be involved in the process of changing the address information?

1. Vendors button
2. Vendors tab in the Vendor Center
3. Address Info tab of the Edit Vendor window
4. Account Settings tab of the Edit Vendor window
5. None of the above

Name:

PART II – PROBLEMS AND REPORTS/PRINTOUTS

P-10-1. Larry's Landscaping & Garden Supply—Setup

Assume Larry's Landscaping & Garden Supply converted from a manual system to *QuickBooks*.

Required

a. How many times did Larry's Landscaping & Garden Supply likely use the *QuickBooks* setup procedures?

_____

_____

_____

_____

b. What are the likely similarities and differences in what you did in setup and what Larry's Landscaping & Garden Supply personnel did in their conversion from a manual system to *QuickBooks*?

_____

_____

_____

_____

_____

Name:

c. Why is it likely that it took Larry's Landscaping & Garden Supply personnel considerably longer to make the conversion to *QuickBooks* than it took you in this project?

_____

_____

_____

_____

_____

_____

d. Why was the Larry's Landscaping & Garden Supply conversion from a manual system to *QuickBooks* most likely done at a year-end instead of during the year?

_____

_____

_____

_____

_____

_____

_____

Name:

e. Assume management decided to convert from a manual system to *QuickBooks* halfway through a year. Describe the process as to how the conversion would likely occur.

_____

_____

_____

_____

_____

_____

_____

_____

P-10-2. Larry's Landscaping & Garden Supply—Accounts receivable setup

You entered all information in *QuickBooks* during setup in a conversion from a manual system to *QuickBooks,* including the transactions that make up the beginning balance in accounts receivable. The debits and credits in the ending balance in the general ledger trial balance are equal. When you compare the accounts receivable total in the general ledger trial balance to the balance in manual system, there is a $5,000 difference. Your assistant suggests that you should make a general journal entry to correct the difference.

Required

a. Can you now change the total in the *QuickBooks* general ledger trial balance to make it equal the balance in the manual system?

_____

_____

b. How can you determine if the difference results from an error in the manual system or the information you entered in *QuickBooks?*

_____

_____

_____

c. If there is an error in the *QuickBooks* accounts receivable balance, what likely caused the error?

_____

_____

d. Explain how you will correct the error if there is one.

_____

_____

_____

_____

P-10-3. Change from a system using *Sage 50 Accounting* to *QuickBooks*

Ablon, Inc., used *Sage 50 Accounting* software for several years and decided to switch to *QuickBooks* at 1/1/2019. Ablon's has 75 employees, 700 customers, 175 vendors, and 250 inventory items.

Required

a. What are the similarities and differences in the conversion from *Sage 50 Accounting* to *QuickBooks* compared to a conversion from a manual system?

_____

_____

_____

_____

_____

_____

_____

_____

Name:

b. Why would the conversion from a manual system be extremely time-consuming whereas the conversion from *Sage 50 Accounting* to *QuickBooks* could be done fairly quickly?

_____

_____

_____

_____

_____

_____

_____

_____

NOTES

NOTES

NOTES

NOTES